A Bedtime Prayer

Sanja Rešček

SCHOLASTIC INC.

This book belongs to:

....

....

....

Thank You, God in heaven,
As we end another day.
We say goodnight, God bless you,
And go along our way.

We stretch and give a yawn
And slowly climb the stairs.
Another day is over.
It's time to say our prayers.

Thank You, God in heaven,
For the stars and moon.
Tucked up in our cozy beds,
We'll be sleeping soon.

We snuggle in our blankets
Surrounded by Your light.
We know that You are watching,
And will keep us safe tonight.

Thank You, God in heaven,
The sun begins to rise.
We open up the curtains
To see the bright blue skies.

With each new day before us,
The songbirds start to sing.
Thank You, God, for all Your gifts
That today will bring.

Thank You, God in heaven,
For creatures great and small.
All things bright and beautiful,
We know You love them all.

From each tiny butterfly,
To the bright bird high above,
You made them in Your wisdom,
And You keep them in Your love.

Thank You, God in heaven,
For our world so sweet.
Thank You for Your bounty,
And for all the food we eat.

Thank You for the garden fruit,
All ripened by the sun.
Apples, plums, and peaches,
You made each and every one.

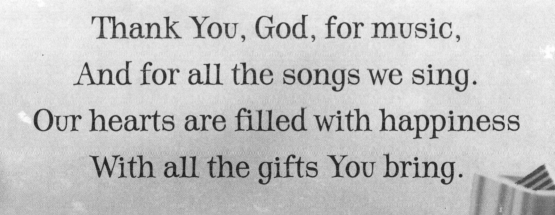

Thank You, God in heaven,
For sweet and simple joys—
Playtime shared with friends,
For laughter, games, and toys.

Thank You, God, for music,
And for all the songs we sing.
Our hearts are filled with happiness
With all the gifts You bring.

Thank You, God in heaven,
For our home, sweet home.
We hold it in our hearts,
No matter where we roam.

You share all of our sunny days,
And give shelter in the storm.
With Your love around us,
We'll be safe and sound and warm.

Thank You, God in heaven,
For all Your love and care.
Thank You for Your wisdom,
And the precious times we share.

You teach me to be kind,
To be patient, good, and strong.
You guide me on the path
To know what's right from wrong.

Thank You, God in heaven,
For those we love so dear,
For our family and friends,
And loved ones, far and near.

We share a kiss and hug,
As we say goodnight.
Thank You, God in heaven,
For watching us tonight.

Thank You, God in heaven,
For all the things You share,
For all Your special gifts,
Here's a thank-you prayer.

The day is at an end,
The moon is shining bright,
We say thank You, dear God above,
And, at last, goodnight.

ISBN 978-0-545-80836-1

12 11 10 9 8 7 6 5 4 3 2   14 15 16 17 18 19/0

Printed in the U.S.A.   40

First Scholastic printing, November 2014